i-SPY

D1633087

London
SPY IT! SCORE IT!

Introduction

London is one of the greatest cities in the world. Its long history and endless variety make it a fascinating city to explore. Evidence of London's past is all around – and is easy to spot. There are sections of Roman settlement still visible in the city dating back 2000 years; the Tower of London dates back 1000 years to William the Conqueror; Sir Christopher Wren's masterpiece, St Paul's Cathedral, dates from the 17th century; the London Eye and the Shard are more recent additions to the skyline and form part of the modern landscape of the ever-changing city. It has too much history and is too large for anyone to know it all but, with i-SPY London, you can get to know it very well – and go on to discover more things for yourself.

How to use your i-SPY book

Keep your eyes peeled for the i-SPYs in the book.

If you spy it, score it by ticking the circle or star.

25 POINTS

Items with a star are difficult to spot so you'll have to search high and low to find them.

If there is a question and you know the answer, double your points. Answers can be found at the back of the book (no cheating, please!).

Once you score 1000 points, send away for your super i-SPY certificate. Follow the instructions on page 64 to find out how.

Sherlock Holmes Museum

The interior of 221b Baker Street, which was the fictional address of the great detective, has been faithfully created exactly as described in the published stories.

10 POINTS

London Zoo

London Zoo, in Regent's Park, is one of the world's most famous zoos and is home to over 20,000 animals. There is a programme of daily talks, giving visitors the opportunity to learn more about the animals from their keepers.

10 POINTS

Madame Tussauds

This museum of waxworks is a major London attraction, where the lack of ropes or barriers allows for real close-up photo opportunities with the rich and famous!

10 POINTS

BBC Broadcasting House

Located on Portland Place, this is the central London headquarters of the BBC's news, radio, television and online services. The building incorporates a memorial called 'Breathing' that commemorates journalists who have been killed while carrying out their work around the world.

20 POINTS

Harley Street

15 POINTS

Harley Street has been associated with medicine since the middle of the 19th century, when doctors were attracted to the large Georgian houses and their proximity to mainline train stations. There are now over 3000 people employed in the private clinics and practices in the area.

Regent's Park

One of the Royal Parks of London and a lovely place to stroll or have a picnic. Look out for some of the wild birds that live here too – there are more than 100 different species.

 10 POINTS

Regent's Park and Marylebone

Oxford Street

Oxford Street is one of the most famous shopping streets in the world.

5 POINTS

Selfridges

First opened in 1909, Selfridges department store dominates the west end of Oxford Street. The clock above the entrance is known as 'The Queen of Time'.

10 POINTS

The Wallace Collection

This art collection include masterpieces by Titian, Rubens, Reynolds, Van Dyke and Canaletto.

20 POINTS

Marble Arch

Marble Arch, designed in 1827 by John Nash, is made of carrara marble – a high-quality whitish-grey marble. It was originally built as the entrance to Buckingham Palace, but it was moved to its current location, at the north-east corner of Hyde Park, in 1851.

10 POINTS

The Serpentine Lake

Peace and serenity is never very far away in London. In Hyde Park, you can take a rowing boat out on this man-made lake or even go for a swim in the lido.

15 POINTS

Hyde Park

10 POINTS

A public park since early in the 17th century, Hyde Park is one of London's most prized open spaces. It has hosted many major music festivals.

Princess Diana Memorial Fountain

Located in the south-west corner of Hyde Park, this is not a fountain in the traditional sense, but a large, oval stream bed.

15 POINTS

Speakers' Corner

Located at the north-east side of Hyde Park, Speakers' Corner is a space for orators and hecklers to debate the issues of the day.

 10 POINTS

Peter Pan Statue

J.M. Barrie, author of the Peter Pan stories, lived near Kensington Gardens. These gardens inspired some of his work, and the boy who never grew up is immortalised in a bronze statue there.

15 POINTS

Albert Memorial

Gleaming in gold leaf following a major restoration project, the Albert Memorial in Kensington Gardens is dedicated to Queen Victoria's husband, who died in 1861.

 15 POINTS

9

Royal Albert Hall

15 POINTS

A major arts venue hosting classical music (including the world famous Proms), rock concerts, ballet, tennis and award ceremonies. It is one of the most atmospheric music venues in the world.

Harrods

Perhaps the most famous shop in the world, it boasts a huge array of products. The food hall on the ground floor houses a vast selection of foodstuffs!

10 POINTS

Harvey Nichols

This is another iconic Kensington store. It started out as a small linen shop in 1831 and now has six floors of fashion and food, including a restaurant on the fifth floor.

10 POINTS

Victoria and Albert Museum

This fine museum is housed on four floors. Endless galleries display fine and applied art collections, sculpture, furniture, fashion and photographs.

15 POINTS

Science Museum

This vast collection includes Helen Sharman's space suit and Caroline Herschel's telescope, as well as interactive displays, flight simulators and an IMAX cinema.

15 POINTS

12

Natural History Museum

This vast museum contains hundreds of exciting interactive exhibits with sections on dinosaurs, ecology and the animal world.

15 POINTS

Kensington Palace

A royal residence since the 17th century and the birthplace of Queen Victoria. Today it is the official residence of several royals including the Duke and Duchess of Cambridge and their children.

15 POINTS

St James's Park

Once one of Henry VIII's many hunting grounds, this is the oldest of London's royal parks. It has some resident pelicans that you can watch being fed every afternoon.

10 POINTS

St James's Palace

Dating back to the first half of the 16th century, this building was designed as a royal residence and Queen Elizabeth II made her first speech as Queen here.

15 POINTS

Florence Nightingale Statue

This statue of the 'Lady with the Lamp' stands in front of the memorial to the Crimean War, in which she famously nursed the wounded soldiers. They are located just off The Mall.

15 POINTS

Green Park

10 POINTS

Green Park opened to the public in 1826 and today is a popular open space for joggers and walkers. Royal gun salutes are sometimes fired from this park.

The Ritz

This is one of the most famous hotels in London. Afternoon tea here may be a little formal so pop into the foyer instead and see where the rich and famous stay.

15 POINTS

Eros

The statue of Eros, the Greek god of love, is located in Piccadilly Circus. It is believed to be the first in the world to be cast in aluminium, and though it was originally designed to depict Eros's twin brother, Anteros, the people of London have always known it as Eros.

10 POINTS

Mayfair and St James's

Fortnum & Mason

Fortnum's first opened in 1707 and continues to be world famous for its high-quality goods. It was the first store in the world to sell Heinz baked beans – in 1886!

15 POINTS

Beadles at Burlington Arcade

The Beadles are a private police force – they have been guarding the shops there since 1819 and can be identified by their Edwardian frock coats and top hats.

20 POINTS

Bond Street

The two halves of this road, known as 'Old' and 'New' Bond Street, have been home to many upmarket boutiques and jewellers since the street became a fashionable place t live in the 18th century.

10 POINTS

Royal Academy of Arts

This art institution in Burlington House stages big, thematic shows and is famous for its summer exhibition.

15 POINTS

Piccadilly Circus

Located at the junction of Piccadilly and Regent Street, Piccadilly Circus has long been a focal point in central London, famous for its neon advertising signs and home to the statue of Eros.

10 POINTS

Admiralty Arch

This is a large building located between The Mall and Trafalgar Square. As the name suggests, traffic and pedestrians pass through an arch incorporated into the building.

15 POINTS

Changing of the Guard

A ceremony that takes place outside Buckingham Palace, usually every day in June and July, and every other day throughout the rest of the year.

15 POINTS

Horse Guards Parade

Originally Henry VIII's tournament ground, there are ceremonies involving the mounted guard that take place here twice a day.

15 POINTS

Buckingham Palace

The Queen's official residence has over 700 rooms and boasts a 39-acre garden. The palace's state apartments are open to the public in summer. If the Royal Standard is flying overhead, the Queen is in residence. Standing in front of the Palace is the Victoria Monument, which is a memorial to Queen Victoria who reigned from 1837 until her death in 1901.

Mayfair and St James's

The Mall

The Mall is famous the world over as 'The Red Road'. It runs from Buckingham Palace to Admiralty Arch.

10 POINTS

Shepherd Market

Tucked away, this square in Mayfair is surrounded by lanes full of cafes, small shops and restaurants. The square is named after Edward Shepherd, who worked on its development between 1735 and 1746.

20 POINTS

Berkeley Square

This large, rectangular open space was made famous by the song 'A Nightingale Sang in Berkeley Square'.

15 POINTS

Clarence House

Named after its first resident, William, Duke of Clarence, this house was designed by John Nash and dates from 1827. It is now the official residence of The Prince of Wales and the Duchess of Cornwall.

20 POINTS

Soho and West End

Regent Street

One of the most famous streets in London, Regent Street is well known for its Christmas lights, usually switched on by a celebrity in November.

10 POINTS

Hamleys

A 'must-visit' for children, this fantastic Regent Street toy store is housed over seven floors and packed with every type of toy imaginable.

 15 POINTS

Liberty

Built in 1924, this mock-Tudor department store on Regent Street is a treasure-trove of fashion, cosmetics, ceramics and printed fabrics.

 20 POINTS

London Palladium

Tucked away in Argyll Street, off Oxford Street, the London Palladium is probably the most famous theatre in the UK and is the venue for many blockbuster productions.

20 POINTS

Carnaby Street

The heartbeat of 'Swinging London' in the 1960s may have lost some of its original charm but it is still a fashionable shopping street.

15 POINTS

Leicester Square

Lined with cinemas, this square is the scene of frequent celebrity-studded film premieres. In the centre of the square, you'll find Leicester Square Gardens.

10 POINTS

Double points if you spot someone famous

23

Soho and West End

Trafalgar Square

This square is dominated by the facade of the National Gallery as well as the 50 m (165 ft) column dedicated to Admiral Lord Nelson. The base is guarded by four massive lions!

St Martin-in-the-Fields

Situated at the corner of Trafalgar Square, this lovely 18th-century building is the parish church of the Royal Family. Originally it was surrounded by fields, which is how it got its name.

National Portrait Gallery

Visit this collection to see history through art — portraits and representations of important figures throughout the ages, including English monarchs since medieval times.

15 POINTS

Charles I Statue

This statue of King Charles I on the south side of Trafalgar Square stands at the point from which all distances to London are measured on road signs around the country.

15 POINTS

15 POINTS

National Gallery

This neo-classical style gallery has a superb collection of European paintings dating from 1250 to 1900. The collection includes works by Botticelli, Leonardo da Vinci, Rembrandt, Gainsborough, Turner, Cezanne and Van Gogh.

Soho and West End

Chinatown

Best seen in the evening, the area around Gerrard Street is home to a vibrant Chinese community with lots of restaurants, supermarkets and souvenir shops.

 10 POINTS

West End Theatre

London's Theatreland is one of the largest theatre districts in the world, with many world famous shows.

10 POINTS

Museum of London

Located on London Wall, this extensive collection depicts the history of London, with Roman artefacts from nearby excavations.

15 POINTS

Frost Fair Mural

Before the building of modern bridges, the River Thames often froze in winter. Underneath Southwark Bridge is a mural of the famous Frost Fair of 1564.

25 POINTS

TOP SPOT!

Royal Courts of Justice

These buildings, built in the Victorian Gothic style, handle many of the nation's major civil court cases. They are located on The Strand.

15 POINTS

27

Guildhall

Guildhall, off Gresham Street, has been the administrative centre of the City of London for almost 900 years. The current building was begun in 1411 and includes a medieval great hall, which is still used for ceremonies and banquets.

15 POIN

Old Bailey

This is the Central Criminal Court of England and Wales. The gold statue on the top is of Lady Justice, who holds a sword in one hand and scales of justice in the other.

15 POINTS

Lincoln's Inn Fields

Lincoln's Inn Fields is the largest public square in London. The chambers of many law firms surround the green area.

20 POINTS

TOP SPOT!

Sir John Soane's Museum

Overlooking Lincoln's Inn Fields, this house contains the private collection of the architect who died in 1837. It includes famous artworks, furniture and artefacts, such as an Egyptian sarcophagus.

25 POINTS

Bank of England

The Bank of England is one of the oldest banks in the world and the issuer of all bank notes for England and Wales.

20 POINTS

Tower Bridge

Tower Bridge has stood over the River Thames since 1894 and is one of the finest, most recognisable landmarks in the world.

10 POINTS

HMS Belfast

A World War II cruiser, with nine decks to explore – everything from the Captain's bridge to the massive boiler and engine rooms. It is moored off the south bank of the River Thames, close to Tower Bridge.

15 POINTS

Tower of London

Originally built by William the Conqueror, the Tower of London has been a fortress and a prison, as well as a palace. The Beefeaters and famous ravens guard the priceless Crown Jewels.

What is the correct title of the Beefeaters?

Double with answer

Barbican

The Barbican is a monolithic cultural centre with an art gallery, cinema, theatre and auditorium. It was opened in 1982 and is an example of the Brutalist style of architecture.

15 POINTS

Tower 42

Located on Old Broad Street, Tower 42 was the first skyscraper to be built in the City.

15 POINTS

The Gherkin

Officially its name is 30 St Mary Axe, or sometimes the Swiss Re Building, but most of us know it as the Gherkin!

10 POINTS

St Paul's Cathedral

Christopher Wren's most famous monument was completed in 1708. It contains the tombs of Nelson and Wellington.

 10 POINTS

Millennium Bridge

The first new bridge across the River Thames since Tower Bridge opened in 1894, and the first ever for pedestrians only. The Millennium Bridge is now an established feature linking St Paul's Cathedral with the Tate Modern.

 15 POINTS

St Katharine Docks

Built in 1828, the docks traded for over 120 years and were closed after larger ships could no longer pass through the lock into the basin.

15 POINTS

The Monument

The Monument stands 60.6 m (199 ft) high and exactly 60.6 m (199 ft) from the spot in Pudding Lane where the Great Fire of London started in 1666. It was built shortly afterwards to commemorate the Great Fire and also to celebrate the rebuilding of the city.

20 POINTS

Big Ben

Probably the most famous landmark in London, Big Ben is actually the nickname of the 14-tonne bell, cast in 1858, of the four-faced clock at the top of the clock tower in the Houses of Parliament.

5 POINTS

Houses of Parliament

5 POINTS

This has been the seat of English government since 1512 and is home to both the House of Commons and the House of Lords. This vast mock-gothic palace was built after a fire destroyed the original building in 1834.

Westminster

Downing Street

This most famous of streets was built by Sir George Downing in 1684. Number 10 has been the official residence of serving British Prime Ministers since 1735.

10 POINTS

Oliver Cromwell Statue

Following the English Civil War, Cromwell took control of the country under the title Lord Protector. In 1649, Cromwell famously abolished Christmas! His statue is outside the Houses of Parliament.

What was Cromwell's nickname?

20 POINTS

Double with answer

Sir Winston Churchill Statue

This massive Parliament Square statue was erected in 1973 and depicts the wartime prime minister, Sir Winston Churchill.

15 POINTS

CHURCHILL

Richard the Lionheart Statue

King Richard I ruled from 1189–1199 even though he spoke little English and spent very little time in England. His statue stands outside the House of Lords.

20 POINTS

The Cenotaph

Built in the 1920s by Sir Edwin Lutyens, this bleak stone memorial commemorates those who died in both World Wars. Wreaths are placed here each year on Remembrance Sunday, which is the closest one to November 11th.

10 POINTS

Statue of Boudicca

The warrior queen of the Iceni tribe rose up against the Romans in AD 61. Her statue stands prominently on the embankment overlooking Westminster Bridge.

15 POINTS

Westminster Abbey

This has been a site of worship for over 1000 years.
The 13th-century abbey is the resting place of countless regal,
military and literary names. Every monarch since William the
Conqueror, except two, has been crowned under its roof.

Cabinet War Rooms

Winston Churchill and the British Government directed troops from these basement offices during World War II. The Cabinet War Rooms form part of the Churchill War Rooms museum on King Charles Street.

15 POINTS

Cleopatra's Needle

Dating from around 1460 BC, this Egyptian obelisk was brought to London from Alexandria (the royal city of Cleopatra) in 1878 and erected on Victoria Embankment to commemorate British victories in the Battle of the Nile and the Battle of Alexandria.

10 POINTS

Battle of Britain Monument

The monument pays tribute to those who took part in the Battle of Britain, fought in the skies over Britain in World War II.

20 POINTS

THE BATTLE OF BRITAIN

Westminster

Somerset House

A major arts and cultural centre close to the River Thames, in winter the central courtyard is home to an open-air ice rink.

15 POINTS

The Savoy

Located on the Strand, the Savoy first opened in 1889. It was Britain's first luxury hotel, and to this day it remains one of the world's finest hotels.

What is unusual about Savoy Court, the entrance road to the hotel?

15 POINTS

Double with answer

Whitehall

A broad street running from Trafalgar Square to Parliament Square, it is the seat of political power and home to many civil servants.

 5 POINTS

Tate Britain

Built by the 19th-century sugar magnate Henry Tate, this gallery on Millbank houses art from the 16th to the 20th centuries.

10 POINTS

London Eye

5 POINTS

Planned as a temporary exhibit for the millennium celebrations, this giant Ferris wheel has proved to be a firm favourite for visitors of all ages.

National Covid Memorial Wall

10 POINTS

This mural, that stretches over half a kilometre of South Bank, consists of thousands of hearts, designed to remember the victims of the COVID-19 pandemic.

London Aquarium

Housed in County Hall, the London Aquarium hosts 14 different aquatic themed zones, which hold over 500 different species of sea creatures.

10 POINTS

Southwark Cathedral

There has been a church on this site since 1086, although it did not become a cathedral until 1905. It houses the most interesting collection of tombs and epitaphs outside of Westminster Abbey.

20 POINTS

Tate Modern

This Art Deco former power station is Britain's national museum of modern and contemporary art, displaying major works by Matisse and Picasso.

10 POINTS

Shakespeare's Globe Theatre

Standing a few hundred metres from the original site, the theatre that presented many of Shakespeare's greatest plays has been lovingly recreated with materials and techniques of 400 years ago.

15 POINTS

OXO Tower

When the makers of OXO beef stock cubes wanted to advertise their product with large illuminated signs in the 1920s, they were refused permission. The result? Build your own advertising! The tower is now known as OXO Tower Wharf and contains shops, restaurants, galleries and design studios.

15 POINTS

The Shard

Towering over the whole of London, this 95-storey building resembles a shard of glass. It contains offices, apartments, restaurants and a hotel, plus an observation deck on the 72nd level.

15 POINTS

Clink Prison Museum

Slang now for any prison, 'The Clink' originally referred to the Clink Prison on Clink Street. However, it is now a museum of the infamous jail.

TOP SPOT!

25 POINTS

Imperial War Museum

The Imperial War Museum on Lambeth Road tells the story of British military conflict from World War I to the present day.

20 POINTS

London Dungeon

The London Dungeon brings the gruesome side of London's history to life with the use of displays, rides and live action. Uncover the truth here about the Great Plague, Jack the Ripper and the Great Fire of London.

15 POINTS

45

South Bank

Borough Market

20 POINTS

London's oldest fruit and vegetable market has existed since at least 1276, and has been on the current site in Southwark Street since the mid-18th century. The market now has over 100 stalls and sells all kinds of interesting food!

Golden Hinde

In St Mary Overie Dock, you will find a full-size replica of Sir Francis Drake's galleon in which he circumnavigated the globe between 1577 and 1580.

20 POINTS

IMAX

This large-format cinema, close to Waterloo Station, features a screen measuring $20 \times 26\,m$ ($66 \times 85\,ft$) – it's the biggest screen in the UK!

20 POINTS

Covent Garden

This is London's oldest planned square, built in the 1630s on the site of the Saxon town of Lundenwic. Long associated with its fruit and vegetable market, Covent Garden now has many shops, bars and restaurants.

10 POINTS

Royal Opera House

Located in Covent Garden, the Royal Opera House has its own orchestra and is home to both the Royal Opera and the Royal Ballet.

15 POINTS

London Transport Museum

Travel through time and learn the history of London's transport system, from 1800 to the present day.

15 POINTS

47

Bloomsbury and Fitzrovia

British Museum

Britain's oldest museum opened in 1759. It contains an array of artefacts illustrating the history of human art and culture from around the world. It is located on Great Russell Street.

10 POINTS

British Library

Situated on Euston Road, the national library of the UK is one of the world's largest research libraries. It contains over 150 million items and receives a copy of every book produced in the UK and Ireland (including this one!).

15 POINTS

BT Tower

With an overall height of 189 m (620 ft), this telecommunications tower became one of the capital's top attractions when it opened in 1965. It closed to the public for security reasons in 1980.

5 POINTS

St Pancras Station

Renovated in the 2000s at a cost of £800 million, the refurbished station is the terminus for Eurostar™ as well as serving the East Midlands of England.

10 POINTS

Outside Central Zone

Battersea Power Station

This famous south bank landmark was designed by Giles Gilbert Scott, who also designed the red telephone box! It was closed in 1983 but is now being redeveloped as apartments, shops, restaurants and offices.

10 POINTS

Cutty Sark

Launched in 1869 for transporting tea back from China, the Cutty Sark travelled the world and was the fastest clipper of her day. She has been moored up in dry dock in Greenwich since 1957.

 15 POINTS

Canary Wharf

Built on the site of the West India Docks, Canary Wharf takes its name from the quay where fruit and vegetables used to arrive from the Canary Islands. It contains three of the UK's tallest buildings.

Do you know their names?

20 POINTS

Double with answer

Wembley Stadium

The world's most expensive football stadium, when completed in 2007, was built on the site of the original Wembley Stadium that had stood since 1923. Most England home international matches are played here as well as all major domestic football finals. Wembley is also home from time to time to other sports such as American football and pop concerts, where the capacity can reach a quarter of a million people!

15 POINTS

Double if you see a match here

Outside Central Zone

Regent's Canal

The canal, now mostly used by pleasure craft, runs from Little Venice near Paddington, through Regent's Park and London Zoo to Camden Town.

20 POINTS

National Maritime Museum

The National Maritime Museum in Greenwich displays an unrivalled collection of maritime artefacts including Horatio Nelson's uniform from the Battle of Trafalgar.

20 POINTS

O2 Arena

Originally a temporary structure built for the millennium celebrations, the O2 Arena in Greenwich is now a major indoor venue for concerts and sporting events.

20 POINTS

Thames Barrier

Built to stop London from flooding, its
10 futuristic gates are supported by seven
concrete piers. It has been operational since
1982 and has been closed around
200 times since then.

TOP
SPOT!

25
POINTS

Iconic London

Guard in bearskin

These helmets, traditionally made of real bearskin, are worn by the Foot Guards of the British Army Household Division, who are responsible for guarding the monarch.

5 POINTS

Dragon

Dragon statues stand guard at several boundary points around the City of London. Most of them are smaller replicas of the two on Victoria Embankment.

15 POINTS

Double-decker bus

London is famous for its red buses and you won't have to wait long before you see one go past. Taking a ride on a double-decker bus is a great way to see the city.

5 POINTS

Newspaper seller

You will sometimes find newspaper sellers on the streets around the centre of London.

5 POINTS

Blue plaque

Over the last 150 years, more than 900 blue plaques have been placed on buildings all over London to mark the famous people who have lived or worked there. How many will you find?

10 POINTS

ENGLISH HERITAGE
SIR ROBERT PEEL
1750 ~ 1830
Manufacturer and reformer
and his son
SIR ROBERT PEEL
1788 ~ 1850
Prime Minister
Founder of the
Metropolitan Police
lived here

Iconic London

Underground sign

These signs mark the entrances to the stations on the London Underground rail network.

5 POINTS

Black taxi

London's official taxis can be seen all over the city. If the yellow sign above the windscreen is illuminated then the taxi is available for hire.

5 POINTS

Phone box

These distinctive red telephone boxes first appeared on the streets of London in 1926 and became widespread around the city, although they are not used as much now as they were in the past.

5 POINTS

Chelsea Pensioner

With their scarlet frock coats and black tricorne hats, the Chelsea Pensioners are a familiar sight around the city. These people are all British Army veterans who live at the Royal Hospital Chelsea.

10 POINTS

Iconic London

Busker

Buskers are people who sing or perform in public places in the hope that passers-by will give them a tip. From bagpipe players to acrobats to living statues, they can be very entertaining.

5 POINTS

Cycle courier

Sometimes the quickest way to get around London is by bike, so cycle couriers are often employed to take letters or parcels directly from one place to another. They usually carry their deliveries in a large bag on their back.

5 POINTS

Any London bridge

There are several road bridges that span the River Thames. Many of them have been rebuilt over the years, but of the city centre bridges that are standing today, the oldest is Westminster Bridge, built in 1862.

5 POINTS

EIIR sign

The Queen's cypher with crown above it can be seen in many places and on many uniforms around the city. The E stands for Elizabeth, the II denotes that she is the second English monarch of that name and the R stands for Regina, which is Latin for Queen.

15 POINTS

Iconic London

Souvenir stall

There are many souvenir stalls around the city where you can buy all sorts of things like T-shirts, keyrings, fridge magnets or ornaments to remind you of your trip to London.

5 POINTS

Beefeater

Beefeater is the nickname given to the Yeoman Warders, who guard the Tower of London, and the Yeoman of the Guard, who play a ceremonial role in many royal events.

5 POINTS

Union Jack

The national flag of the United Kingdom is a familiar sight in London. It incorporates the crosses of the patron saints of England, Scotland and Northern Ireland – the Welsh flag isn't represented because when the Union Jack was first created in 1606, Wales was part of England.

5 POINTS

London Marathon

This race takes participants on a 26.2 mile tour of the city: through Greenwich, over Tower Bridge to the Docklands, then along the Embankment to end on The Mall. It is a prestigious race to win for a professional athlete, but most of the thousands of runners are there for fun or to raise money for charity.

Iconic London

River boat

This is the Thames River Bus. This operates between Hampton Court in the west and Woolwich in the east, and is a good way to see the sights along the river.

5 POINTS

Pub

The typical London pub is on a street corner and is a place where local people and visitors can have a drink and a chat.

5 POINTS

Index

Answers: **P31** Tower of London, Yeoman Warders, **P36** Oliver Cromwell, Old Ironsides, **P40** The Savoy, it is the only road in the UK where vehicles are required to drive on the right, **P50** Canary Wharf, One Canada Square (Canary Wharf Tower), 8 Canada Square, Citygroup Centre.

i-SPY

How to get your i-SPY certificate and badge

Let us know when you've become a super-spotter with 1000 points and we'll send you a special certificate and badge!

Here's what to do:

✓ Ask an adult to check your score.

✓ Apply for your certificate at www.collins.co.uk/i-SPY (if you are under the age of 13 we'll need a parent or guardian to do this).

✓ We'll email your certificate and post you a brilliant badge!